Fabulous Doodles

Buster Books

Illustrated by Nellie Ryan

First published in Great Britain in 2008 by Buster Books,
an imprint of Michael O'Mara Books Limited,
9 Lion Yard, Tremadoc Road,
London SW4 7NQ

A CIP catalogue record for this book is available from the British Library.

ISBN: 978-1-906082-31-4

2 4 6 8 10 9 7 5 3 1

Printed and bound in China by Imago

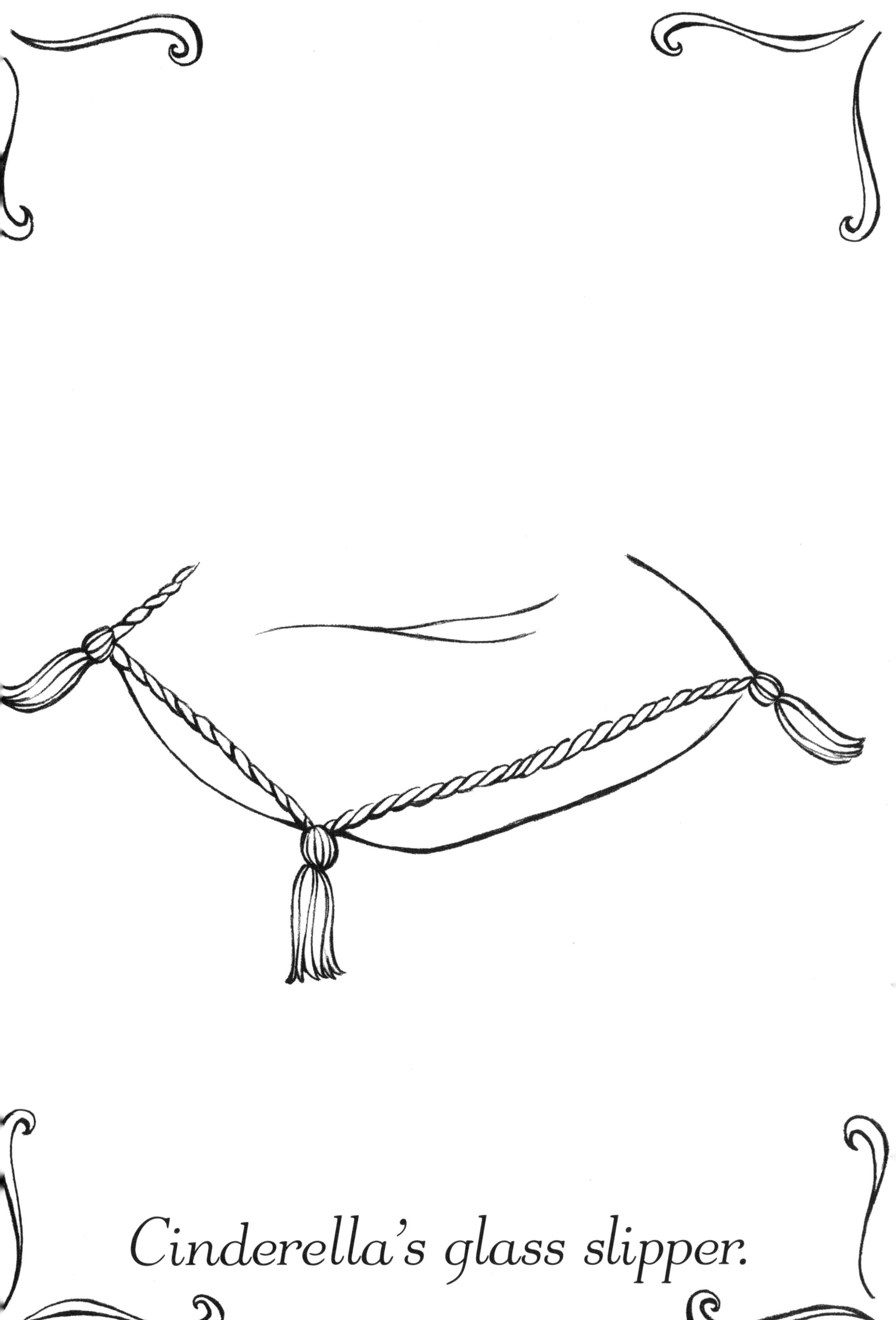

Cinderella's glass slipper.

Decorate the gypsy caravan.

Fabulous perfume bottles.

Finish the Russian dolls.

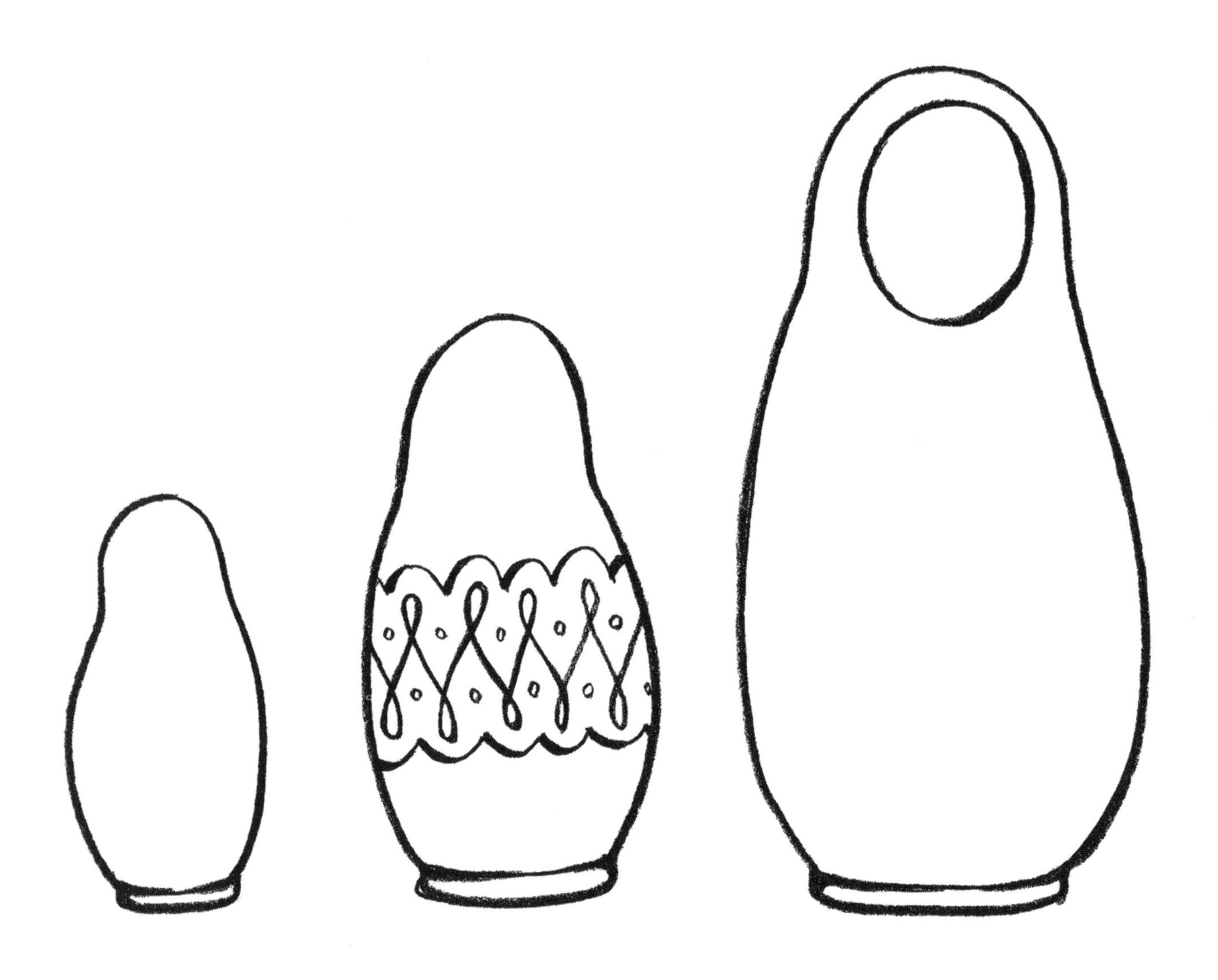

Fill the page with butterflies.

Such gorgeous gift boxes!

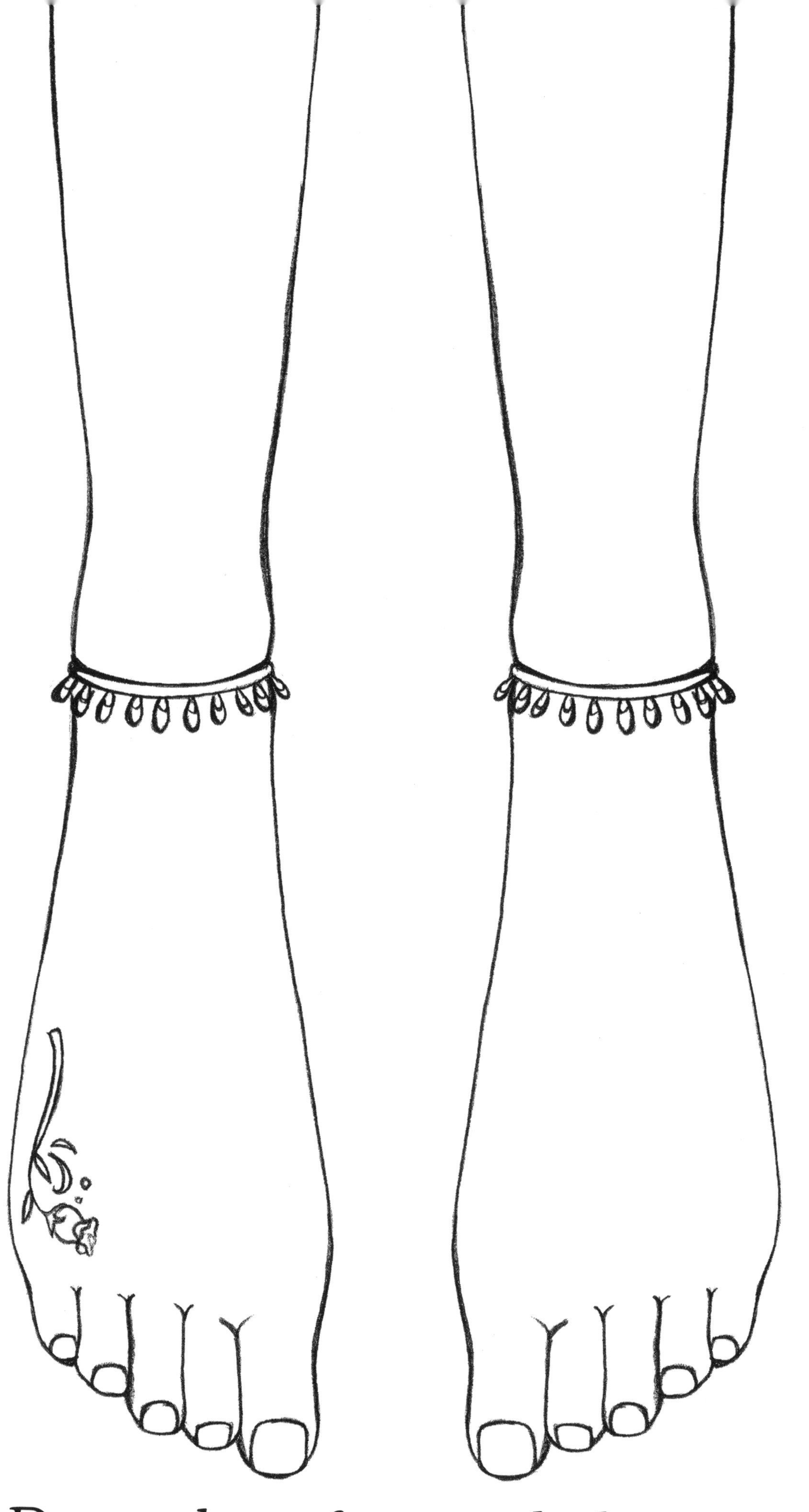

Paint her feet with henna.

Fill the stall with flowers.

What can they see down there?

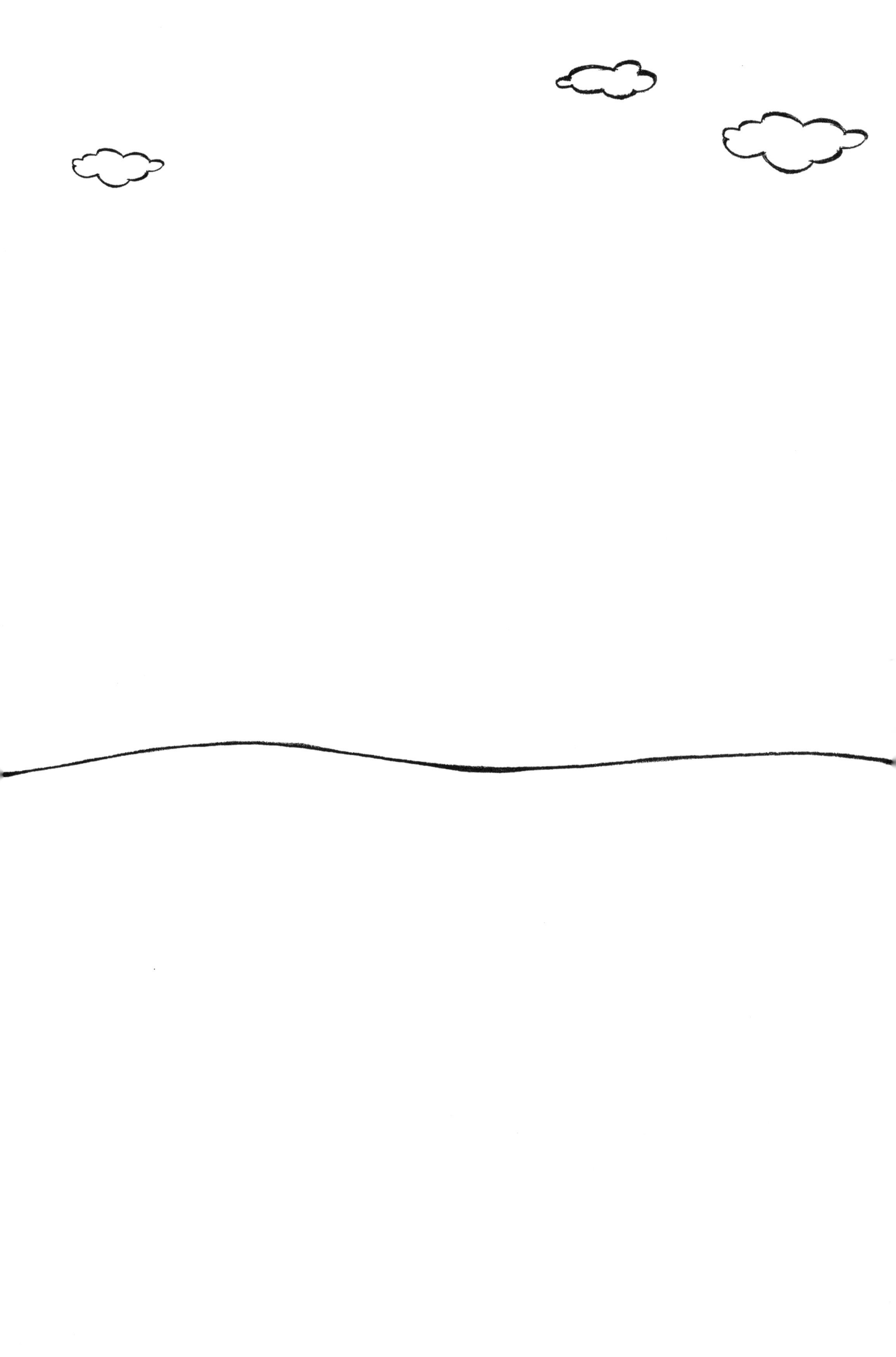

Catch it!

Buckles or bows?

Lots of beautiful rings.

Fill the page with falling leaves.

Lovely lanterns.

Grow a beautiful bonsai tree.

Create your own coat of arms.

Decorate her scooter.

What is she daydreaming about?

Teepee-tastic!

What a breathtaking ball gown.

Decorate the cake.

What a gorgeous kimono!

Complete the girls' costumes.

Funk up her beach towel.

Fill the page with your favourite food.

Customize my snowboard.

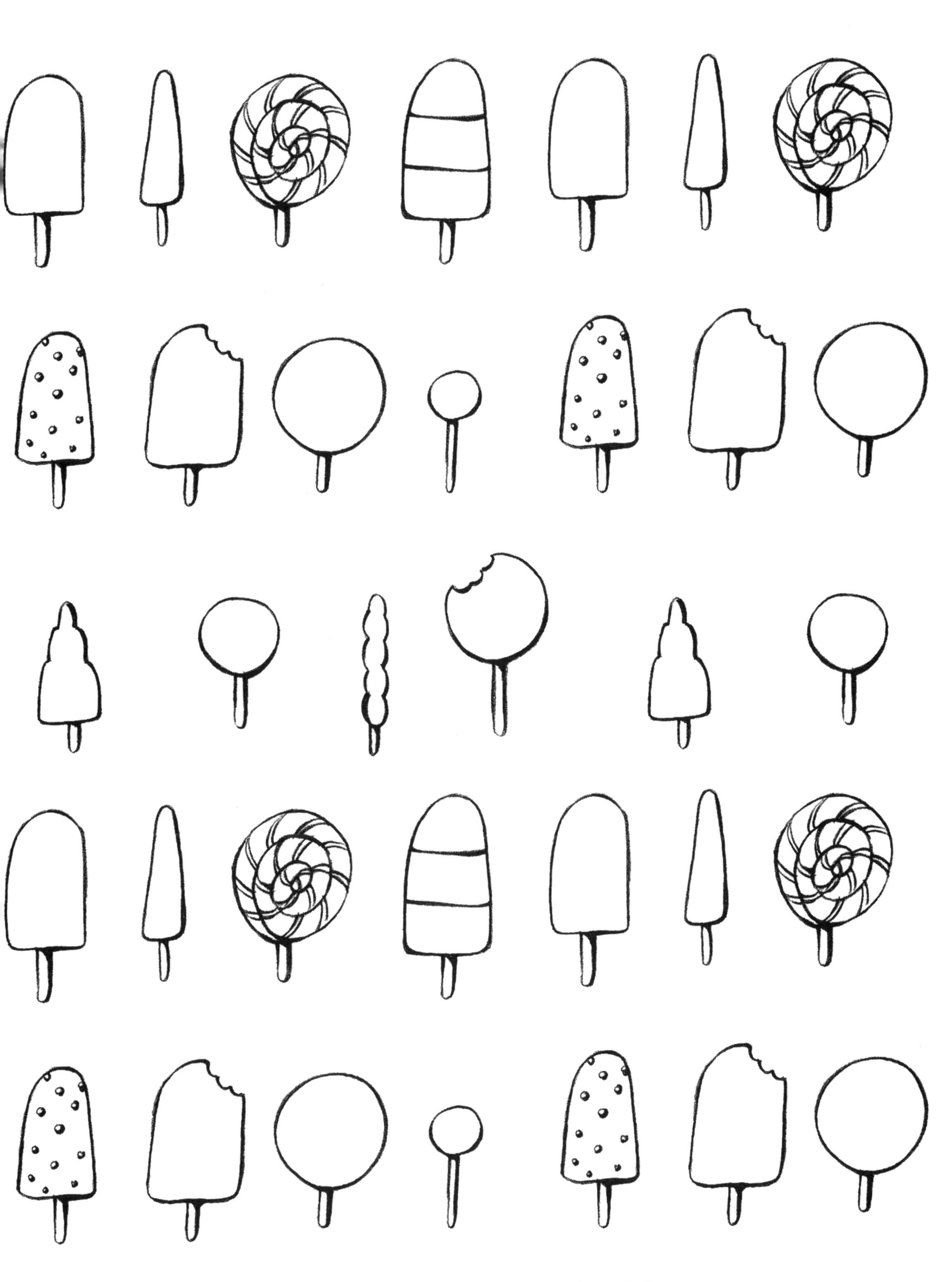

Decorate the lollies.

Super-stylin' surfboards.

Put patterns on the teacups.

Give me a fancy collar and coat.

Fabulous frills.

Create an art exhibition.

Finish the four-poster bed.

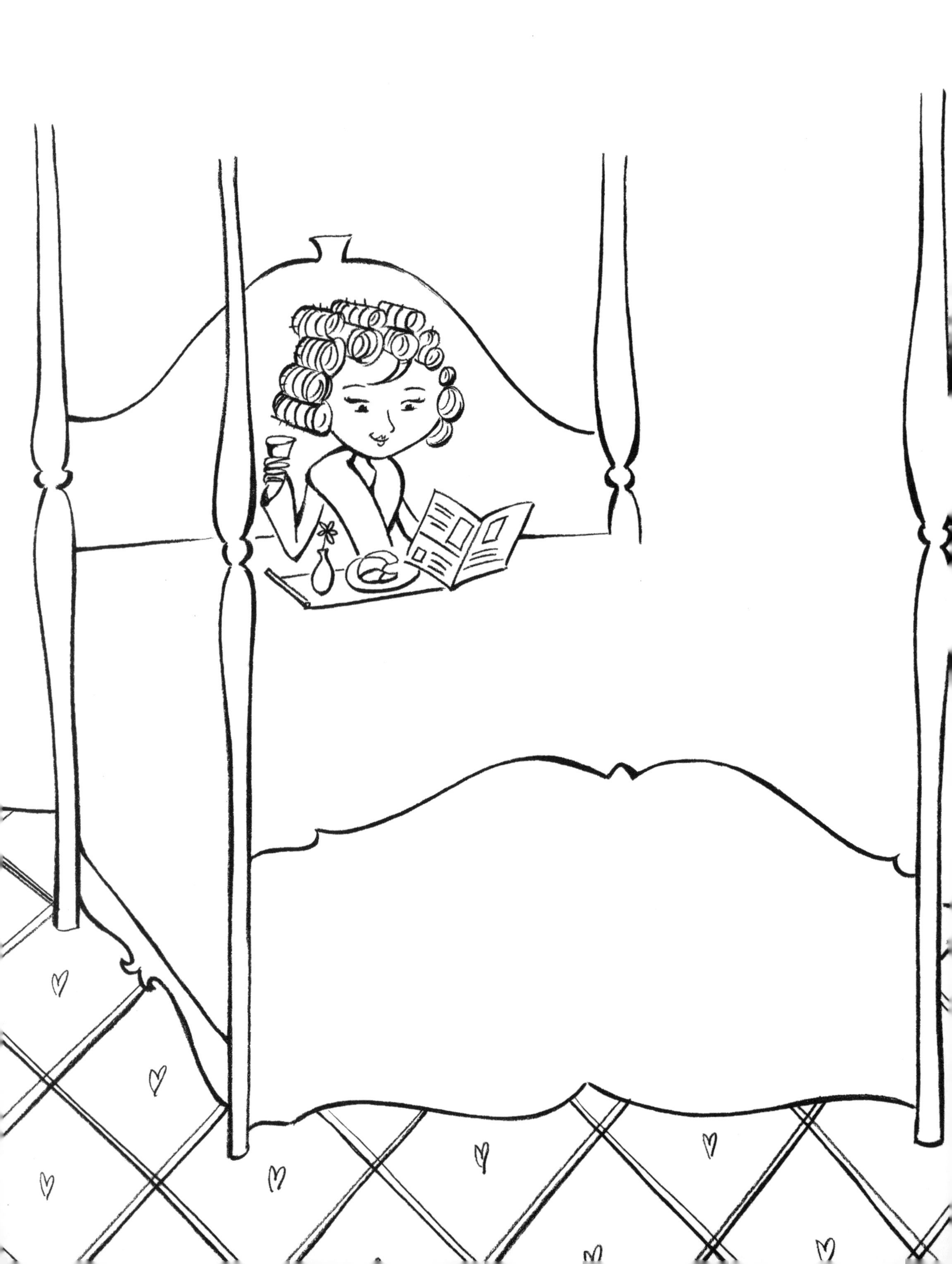

Hand paint these hearts.

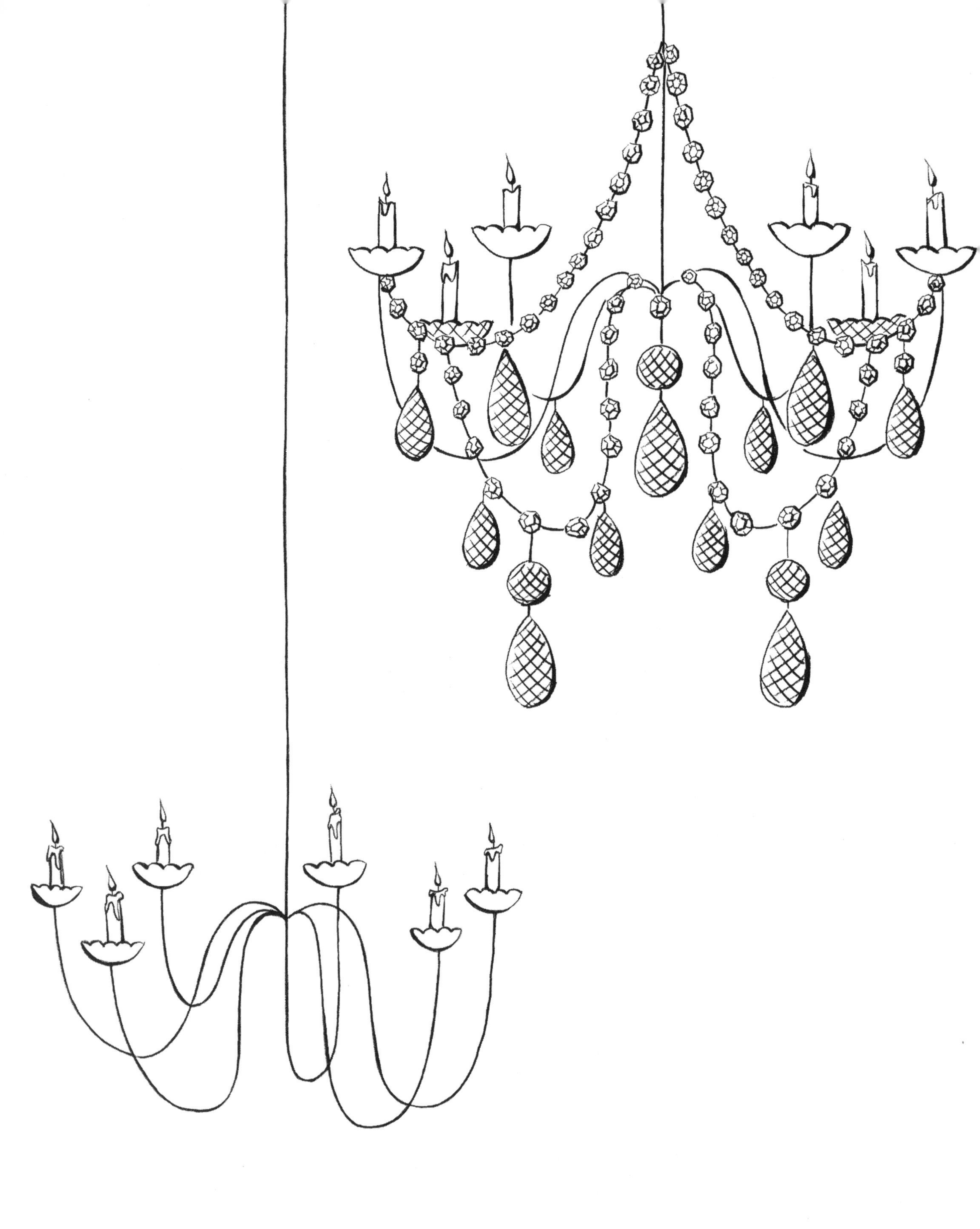

Create a crystal chandelier.

Give her a headdress of flowers.

Fill the page with flowers.

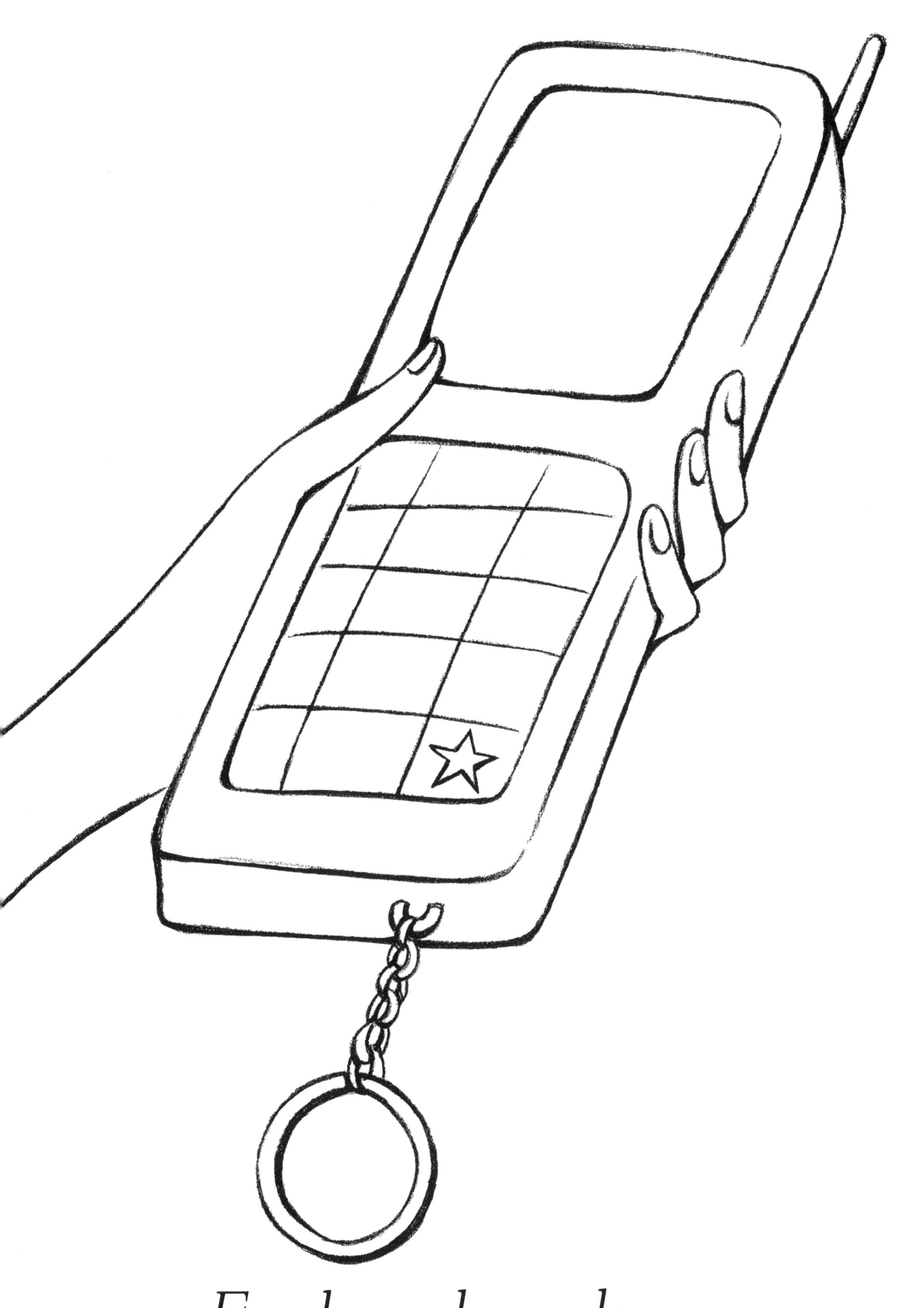

Funk up her phone.

Super-stylin' ice skates.

Glam up her rain gear.

Who is in her gondola?

Fill the box with buttons.

Make a magical mobile.

Grow the other orchids.

What an amazing ice sculpture!

Draw the mermaids
at the party.

Finish the queen's costume.

Dress the pirate.

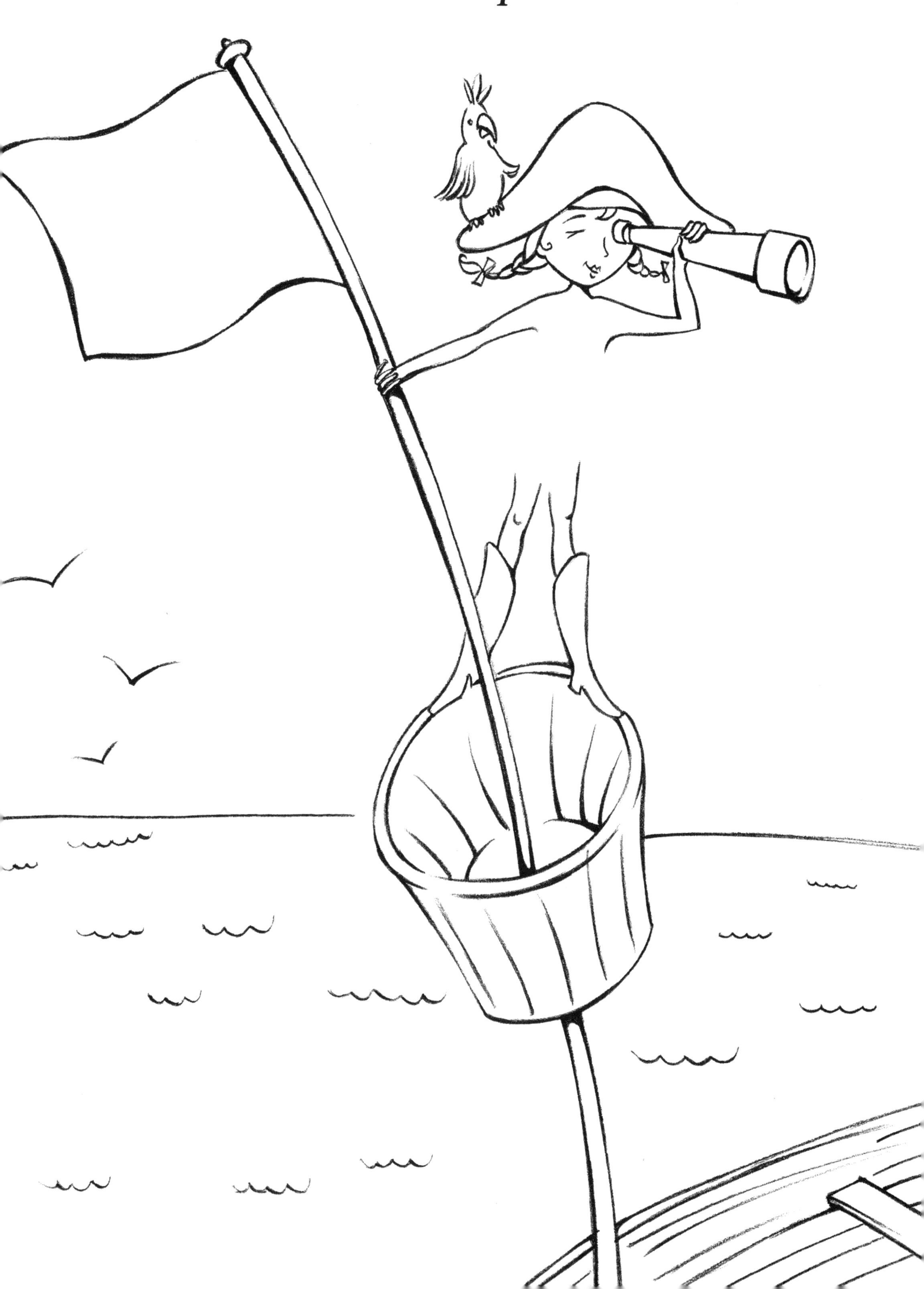

Finish the princess' carriage.

Style the horse's mane and tail.

What is she pulling?

Fill the floating market.

What a beautiful bag.

Decorate the merry-go-round.

What does her limo look like?

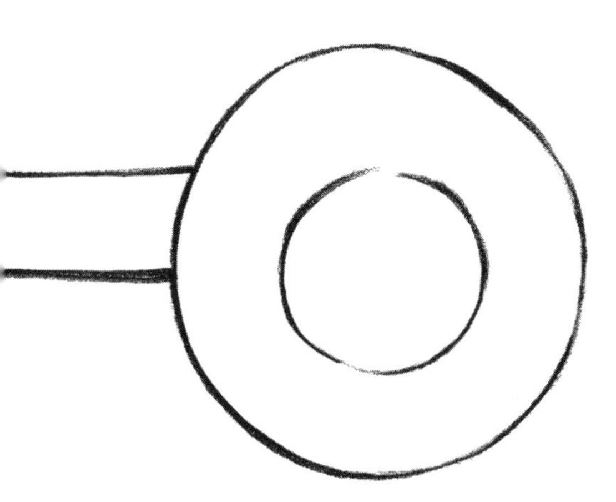

Fabulous fireworks!

What is she carrying?

A billion beautiful bows.

Picnic time!

What is in the attic?

Who is on the red carpet?

The latest hairstyle.

Bon appetit.

What are the band wearing?

Decorate the tights.

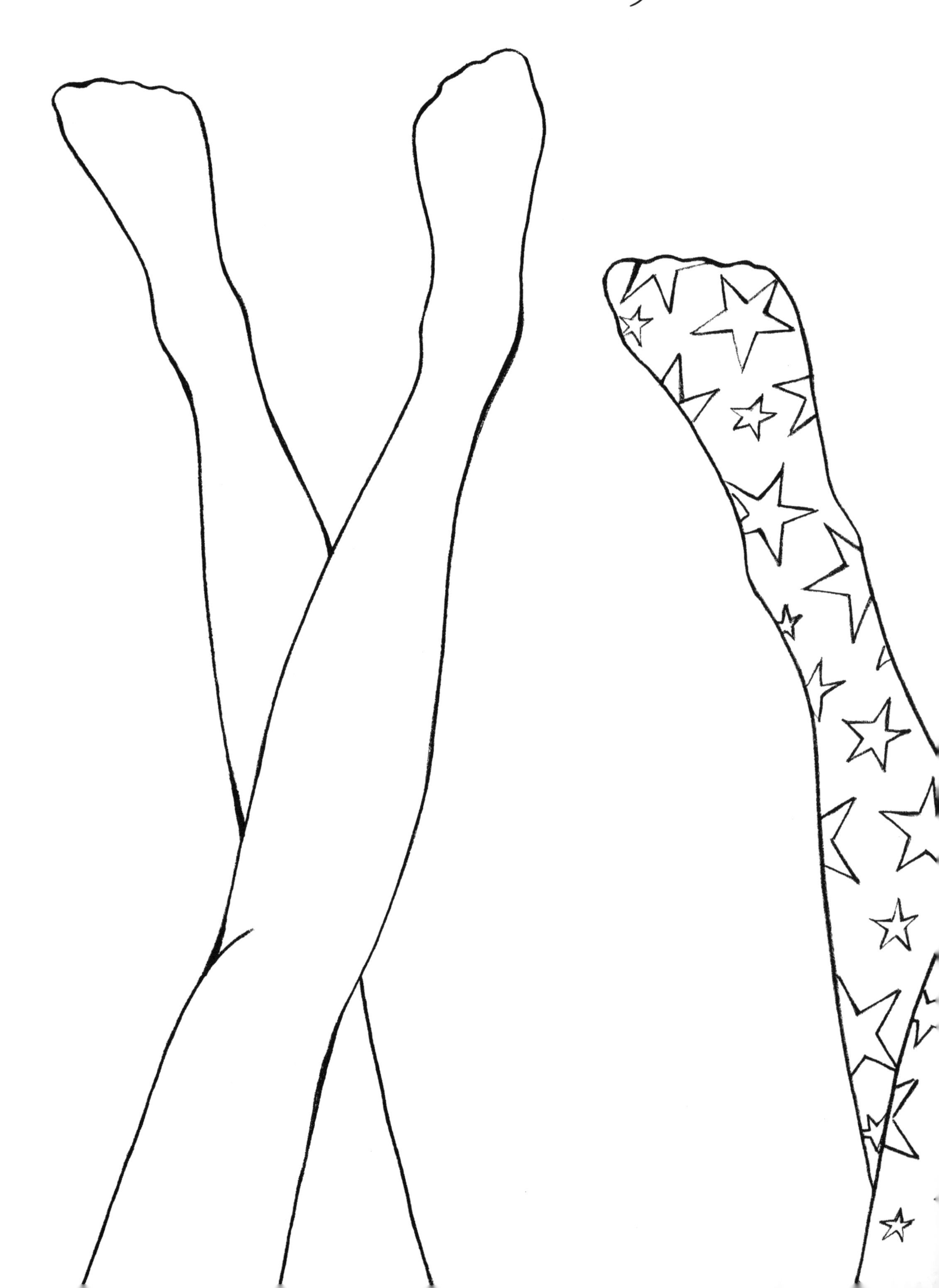

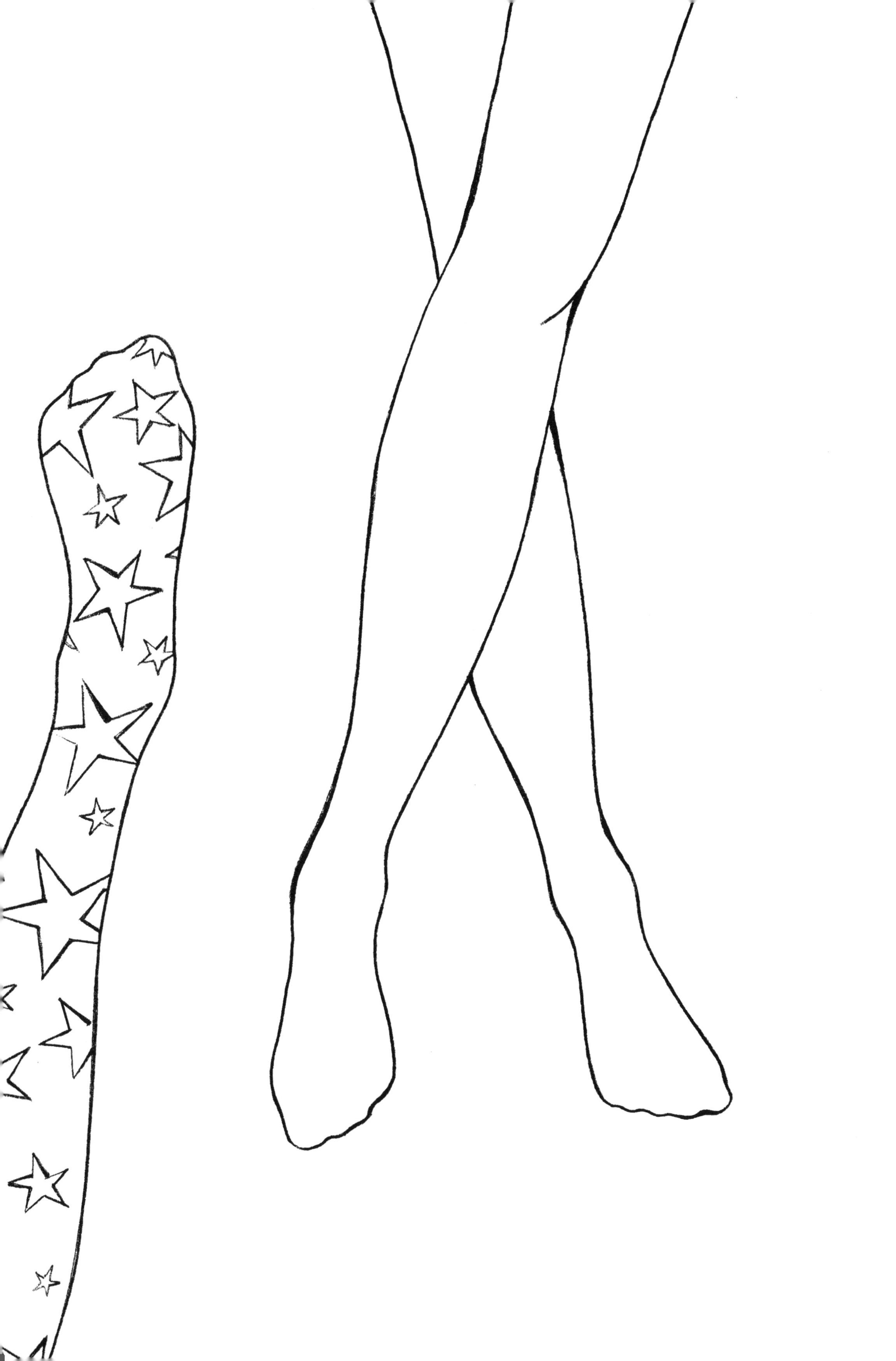

Twelve dancing princesses.

Allacazam!

Create a window display.

What a magical tent!

What is in the locket?

Where has she been shopping?

Decorate the dancer's skirt.

Customize her school uniform.

Fill her beautiful boudoir.

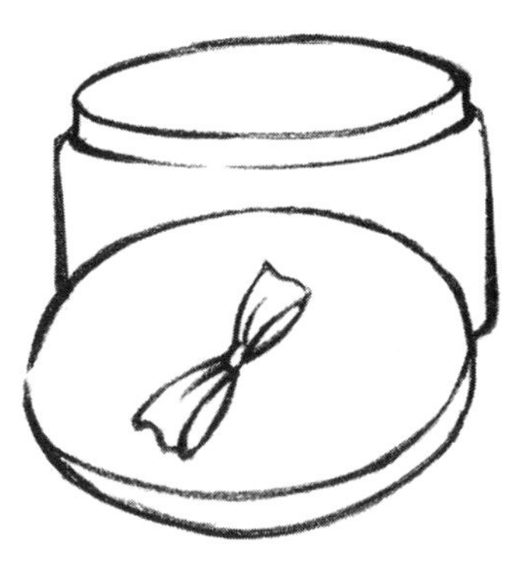

Decorate their masks and gowns.

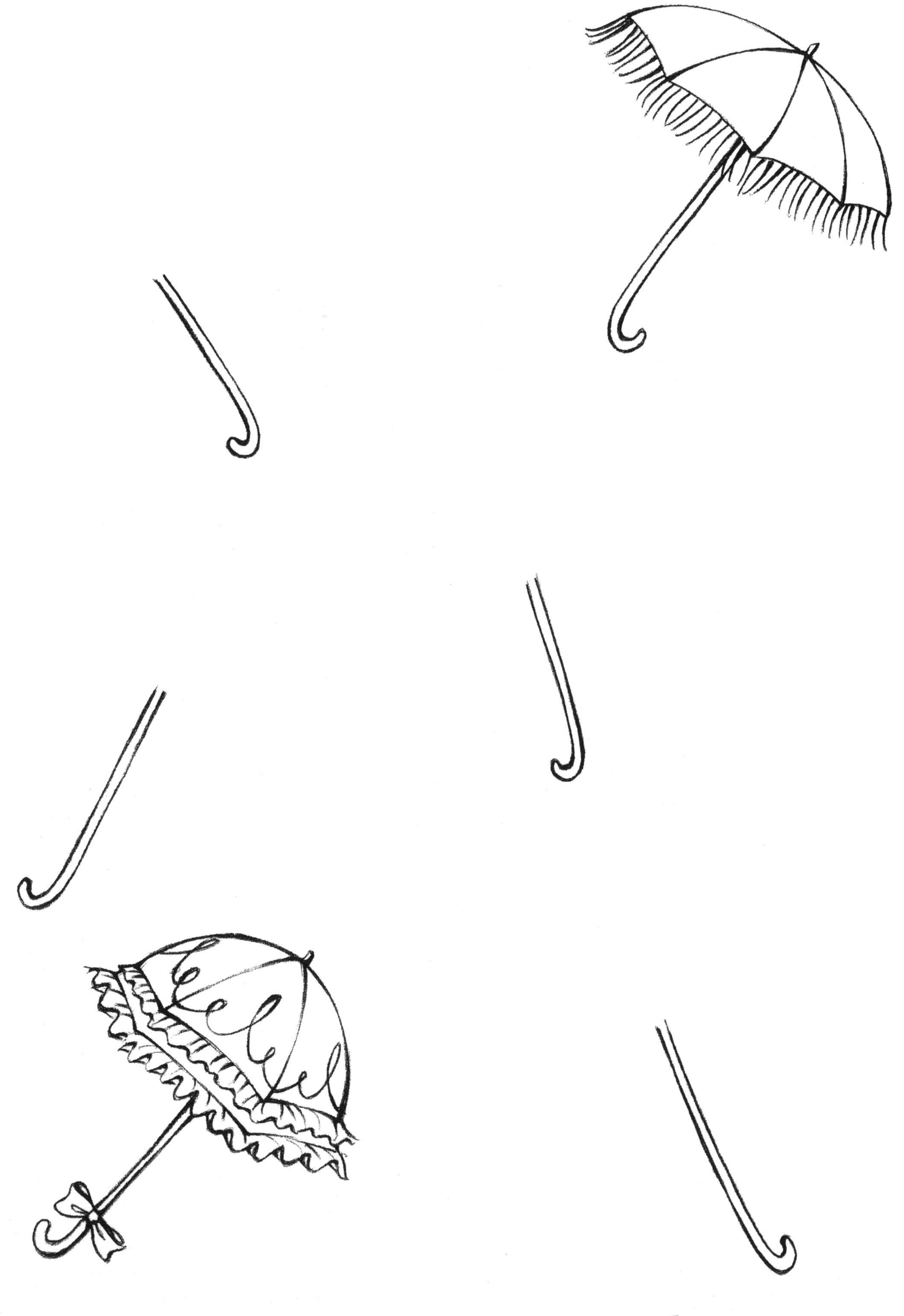

Such pretty parasols!

Add the castle's turrets.

A throne fit for a princess.

Sensational sunnies!

Lots of love.

Design the perfect outfit.

What sensational swimsuits.

Cover the garland with flowers.

Finish the patchwork quilt.

What pretty shoes!

Ice the biscuits.

What fantastic feathers!

A fire-breathing dragon.

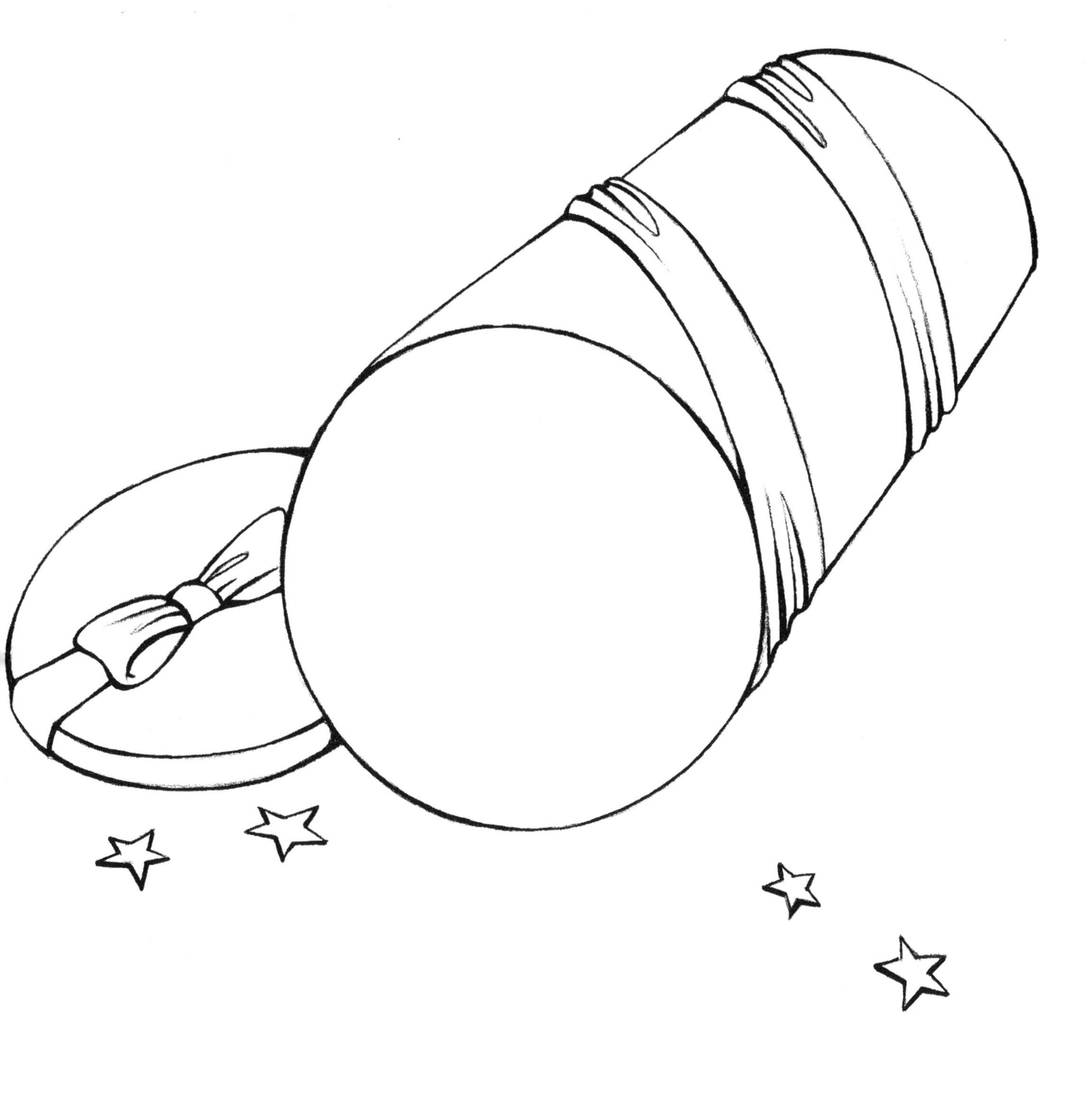

What is in the time capsule?

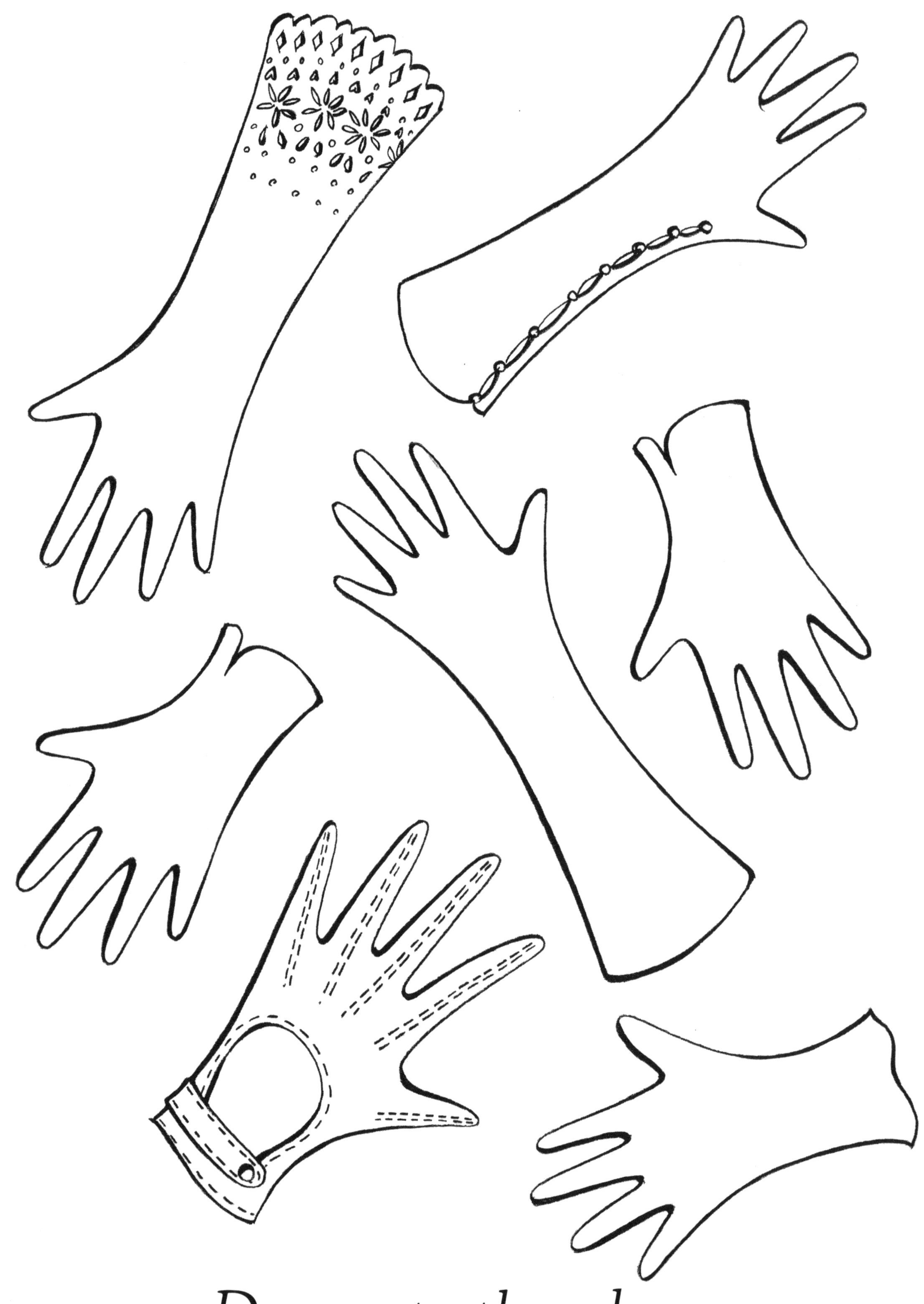

Decorate the gloves.

Design her tutu.

Paint the toy maker's toys.

Finish the fans.

Complete the chorus line's costumes.

What is growing in her garden?

Add an amazing table decoration.

Hall of mirrors.

What is the waiter serving?

Fill the shop with hats.

What amazing vases!

Where is she heading?

Give them fabulous hairstyles.

Yummy!

A beautiful fountain.

Who is riding the elephant?

Fill in her fairy friends.

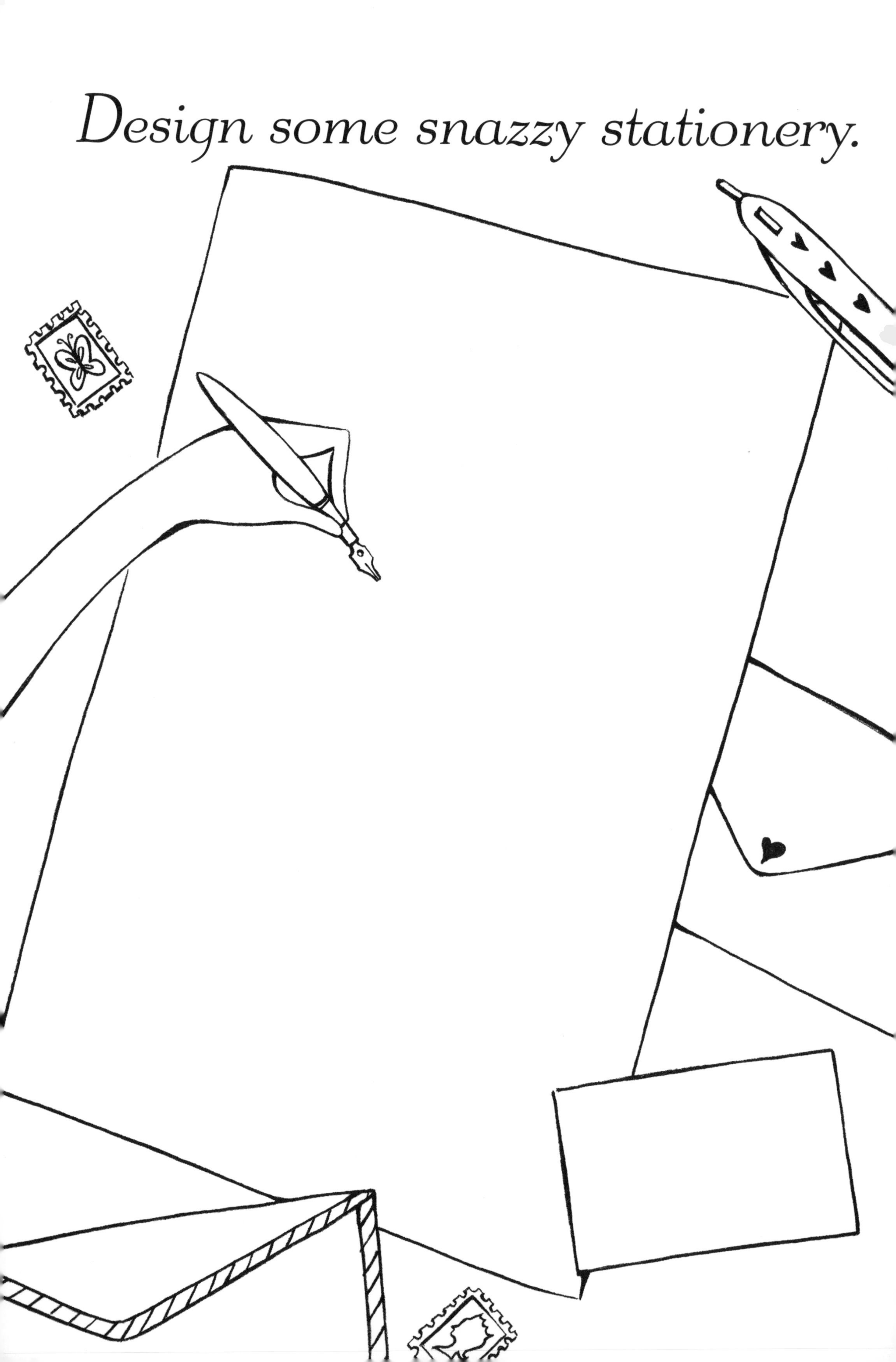
Design some snazzy stationery.

Frame the mirrors.

What are they filming?

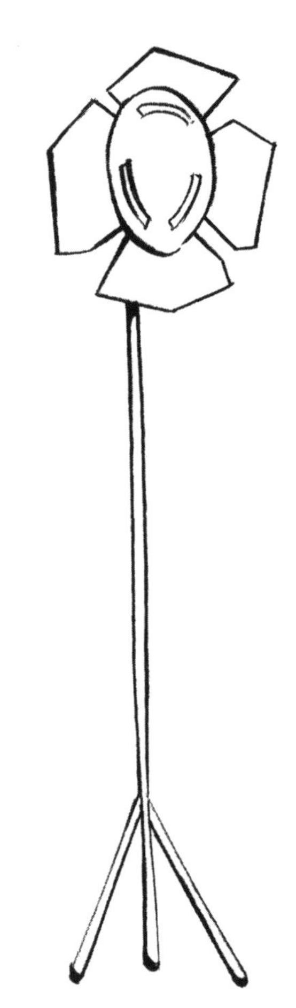

A stormy snow globe.

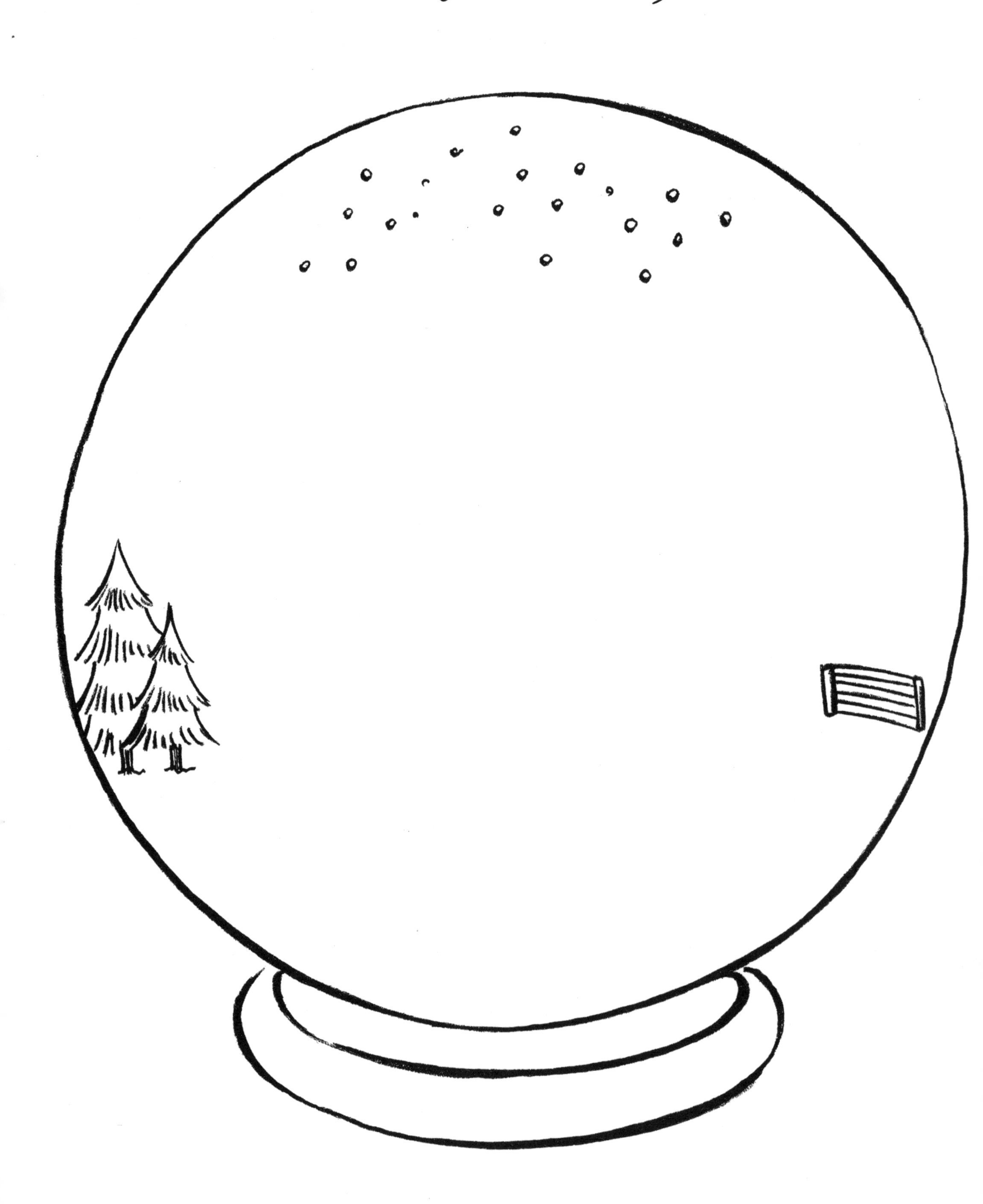